699

The Story of
HIAWATHA

Adapted from Longfellow
by ALLEN CHAFFEE

Illustrated by ARMSTRONG SPERRY

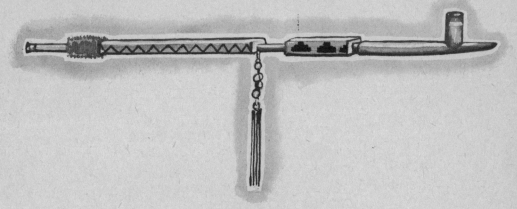

Prepared under the supervision of
JOSETTE FRANK,
Children's Book Adviser
of the Child Study Association of America

RANDOM HOUSE · NEW YORK

THE PEACE-PIPE

ONCE, long ago, Gitche Manito, mighty God of the Indians, came down from Heaven. Standing on the crags of the great Red Pipe-stone Quarry, he looked out upon the country of his people. He would call all the tribes together.

From the red stone of the quarry he made a giant pipe-bowl. He pulled a long reed from the river for a pipe-stem. He filled the mighty pipe with the bark of the red willow, and breathed upon it until it burst into flame. Then, standing erect on the mountain, he smoked the pipe of peace as a signal to the tribes.

The smoke rose high above the mountaintops. The red men saw it, and said to one another:

"Gitche Manito is calling us." All the tribes obeyed the signal: the Delawares and the Mohawks, the Choctaws and Comanches, the Shoshones and the Blackfeet, the Pawnees and Omahas, the Mandans and Dacotahs, the Hurons and Ojibways. They came down the rivers, through the forest, from the prairies and over the mountains.

There they stood on the meadow with all their weapons and in all their war-paint, glaring angrily at one another. Gitche Manito looked upon them lovingly yet sadly. These were his children, his quarrelsome children. Stretching his right hand over them, he said:

"O my poor children, listen to my words of warning. I have given you lands to hunt in. I have given you streams to fish in. I have given you bear and buffalo, reindeer, and wild fowl. Why, then, do you hunt each other? I am tired of your quarrels, of the wars that go on among you. Be at peace from now on, and live together as brothers. I shall send you a leader to guide and teach you. His name will be Hiawatha. He will work with you, and if you listen to him, all will be well. Now wash the war-paint from your faces, and smoke the pipe of peace together."

The Indians obeyed. They broke their arrows and buried their clubs. In the stream they washed away their war-paint. They smoked peace-pipes. And the great Gitche Manito, smiling, rose toward heaven and vanished in the smoke from the peace-pipes.

YEARS passed, and the words of Manito were forgotten. Only the brave Mudjekeewis remembered them.

Now, in the country of the North Wind, the huge bear, Mishe-Mokwa, had his cave. The great bear came by night to kill the red men. But none dared to hunt him.

Mudjekeewis set out to kill the bear. Taking his war-club, he went alone to the cave of Mishe-Mokwa. The great bear was lying asleep on top of a mountain. His claws were red with blood. Around his neck hung a belt of wampum—Indian money made from sea shells.

Mudjekeewis swung his war-club and broke the skull of Mishe-Mokwa. Then the warrior put on the belt of wampum to show his people.

They were proud of him and cried out, "Glory to you! From now on we shall call you West Wind, ruler of all the air!"

Thus was Mudjekeewis chosen Father of the Winds of Heaven. He kept the West Wind for himself, and gave the others to his children. To one he gave the soft East Wind, to another the warm South Wind; and to still another the wild and cold North Wind.

HIAWATHA'S CHILDHOOD

IT happened that Nokomis, beautiful daughter of the Moon, was playing one evening on the moon with her maidens, swinging in a swing of grapevines. One of her maidens, jealous of Nokomis, cut the grapevine and Nokomis fell down, down onto the prairie.

"See! A star is falling from the sky!" the people said.

There among the prairie lilies a daughter was born to Nokomis. And the daughter grew to be tall and slender and beautiful. Her mother warned her often:

"O, beware of Mudjekeewis,
Of the West Wind, Mudjekeewis,
Listen not to what he tells you . . .
Lest the West Wind come and harm you!"

But the maiden did not heed the warning, and Mudjekeewis won her heart. A son was born to them — the little Hiawatha.

Then great sorrow came to Nokomis's daughter; for Mudjekeewis left her and flew back to the kingdom of the West Wind. Hiawatha's gentle mother, broken-hearted, died.

So it was that old Nokomis, Hiawatha's grandmother, took the baby Hiawatha to her wigwam,

> By the shores of Gitche Gumee,
> By the shining Big-Sea-Water . . .

Nokomis made a cradle for Hiawatha of little branches from the linden tree. She tied the branches together with sinews of the reindeer the hunters had brought home for meat. Then she wove in long grasses from the river bank. She lined the cradle with soft moss.

> There the wrinkled, old Nokomis
> Nursed the little Hiawatha,
> Rocked him in his linden cradle . . .

> Stilled his fretful wail by saying,
> "Hush the Naked Bear will hear thee!"
> Lulled him into slumber, singing,

> "Ewa-yea! my little owlet!
> Who is this, that lights the wigwam?
> With his great eyes lights the wigwam?
> Ewa-yea! my little owlet!"

Many things Nokomis taught him.

When little Hiawatha woke at night, Nokomis told him of the stars. She pointed out the comet, Ishkoodah. Hiawatha thought Ishkoodah was like a falling star that trailed shining long hair behind her.

On frosty winter nights Nokomis showed Hiawatha the Northern Lights. They seemed to him like warriors dancing with fiery plumes and war-clubs.

Nokomis showed him the Milky Way, leading across the sky. It was like the broad white road in heaven, he thought.

> At the door on summer evenings
> Sat the little Hiawatha;
> Heard the whispering of the pine trees,
> Heard the lapping of the water,
> Sounds of music, words of wonder;
> "Minne-wawa!" said the pine trees,
> "Mudway aushka!" said the water.
> Saw the fire-fly, Waw-wah-taysee,
> Flitting through the dusk of evening,
> With the twinkle of its candle
> Lighting up the brakes and bushes.
>
> And he sang the song of children,
> Sang the song Nokomis taught him;
> "Wah-wah-taysee, little fire-fly,
> Little, flitting, white-fire insect,
> Little, dancing, white-fire creature,
> Light me with your little candle,
> Ere in sleep I close my eyelids!"

Hiawatha was curious about many things and asked Nokomis many questions. One night as he watched the moon rise from the water, he noticed the flecks and shadows on it.

"What is that, Nokomis?" he asked.

And the good Nokomis answered: "Once a warrior, very angry, seized his grandmother, and threw her up into the sky at midnight. Right against the moon he threw her. It's her body that you see there."

Once, after a rainfall, Hiawatha saw a rainbow arched across the sky.

"What is that, Nokomis?" he asked.

And the good Nokomis answered: "It's the heaven of flowers you see there. When the wild-flowers of the forest and the lilies of the prairie fade and perish on earth, they blossom in that heaven above us."

When he heard the owls at midnight hooting and laughing in the forest, Hiawatha cried out in terror, "What is that, Nokomis?"

And the good Nokomis answered: "That's only the owl and owlet, talking and scolding at each other in their own language."

Soon the little Hiawatha, listening to the birds, learned to talk with them.

699

Learned of every bird its language,
Learned their names and all their secrets,
How they built their nests in summer,
Where they hid themselves in winter,
Talked with them whene'er he met them,
Called them "Hiawatha's Chickens."

He learned, too, the language of all the animals.

Learned their names and all their secrets,
How the beavers built their lodges,
Where the squirrels hid their acorns,
How the reindeer ran so swiftly,
Why the rabbit was so timid,
Talked with them whene'er he met them,
Called them "Hiawatha's Brothers."

Now the woods were full of deer. The red men hunted deer for their meat. They had only bows and arrows to hunt with. For this was long ago.

One old man of the tribe, a friend of Nokomis, was a wonderful story-teller. They called him Iagoo, the great booster, for he boasted of the deeds that other men had done.

"You will be a mighty hunter," he told Hiawatha. "And I will sing your praises far and near."

Then Iagoo set to work and made a bow and some arrows for Hiawatha. The bow he made from a branch of the ash tree. For a string he used a strip of the deer's skin. The arrows he made from an oak bough. At one end they had sharp tips of flint; at the other end were feathers.

Iagoo gave the bow and arrows to Hiawatha, saying, "Go, my son, into the forest, and kill a deer for us!"

Walking softly in his moccasins, Hiawatha went into the forest. And because he knew their language, he knew what all the animals were saying.

Forth into the forest straightway
All alone walked Hiawatha
Proudly, with his bow and arrows;
And the birds sang round him, o'er him,
"Do not shoot us, Hiawatha!"
Sang the robin, the Opechee,
Sang the bluebird, the Owaissa,
"Do not shoot us, Hiawatha!"

Up the oak-tree, close beside him,
Sprang the squirrel, Adjidaumo,
In and out among the branches
Coughed and chattered from the oak-tree,
Laughed, and said between his laughing,
"Do not shoot me, Hiawatha!"

And the rabbit from his pathway
Leaped aside, and at a distance
Sat erect upon his haunches,
Half in fear and half in frolic,
Saying to the little hunter,
"Do not shoot me, Hiawatha!"

But Hiawatha paid them little heed. His thoughts were of the red deer. His eyes were fastened on their tracks, leading downward to the river. He followed the tracks a little way and then hid in the alder bushes. There he waited. And his heart within him fluttered and trembled like the leaves above him.

Then he saw two antlers lifted as a deer came down the pathway. Hiawatha rose on one knee and aimed an arrow. Scarcely

a twig moved with his motion, scarcely a leaf was stirred or rustled, yet the deer heard. It stopped and listened; but it was too late. Hiawatha had drawn back on the bow, and his arrow found its mark.

No longer did Hiawatha feel timid. He felt like a mighty hunter as he bore the red deer homeward. And Iagoo and Nokomis hailed his coming with rejoicing.

From the red deer's hide Nokomis
Made a cloak for Hiawatha,
From the red deer's flesh Nokomis
Made a banquet in his honor.

All the village came and feasted,
All the guests praised Hiawatha,
Called him "Strong-Heart, Soan-ge-taha!"
Called him "Lion-Heart, Mahn-go-taysee!"

HIAWATHA AND MUDJEKEEWIS

HIAWATHA grew swift of foot. He could run faster than the arrow shot from his bow. He could shoot ten arrows upward so swiftly that the tenth one left the bow-string before the first fell to earth.

He had magic mittens made of deer-skin. When he wore them, he could break rocks with his hands.

He had magic moccasins. When he tied them on his feet, each step carried him a mile.

Many times he asked Nokomis about his mother, and heard how Mudjekeewis had left her and how she had died broken-hearted. And his heart burned with anger.

As he grew to young manhood, Hiawatha told Nokomis, "I will go to Mudjekeewis, to the doorway of the West Wind. I will punish him."

Old Nokomis warned him, "He may harm you with his magic! He may kill you with his cunning!"

But the fearless Hiawatha paid no heed to all her warning. So he dressed himself for travel in his deer-skin shirt and leggings. On his head he wore his eagle feathers; on his feet his magic moccasins. In his hand he carried his bow of ash-wood; in his quiver were his strong arrows.

Westward he traveled, a mile at each step. He crossed the Mississippi River. He left the plains behind him.

Soon he reached the Rocky Mountains, Kingdom of the West Wind. And there upon a stormy peak sat Mudjekeewis, his long white hair streaming wildly about him.

When he looked on his son Hiawatha, the old man saw himself as he had once been. "Welcome," he said, "to the Kingdom of the West Wind."

Then the mighty Mudjekeewis boasted of his bravery. He told of his dangerous adventures, and how none could overcome him.

Hiawatha listened, and no word or look betrayed him. But his heart still burned with anger.

"O Mudjekeewis," he asked at last, "is there nothing that can harm you!"

The mighty Mudjekeewis answered, "Only the black rock yonder."

The old man looked with pride at Hiawatha's tall and graceful figure. And he asked, "O Hiawatha! Is there anything you are afraid of?"

Hiawatha, crafty, clever, answered falsely: "Nothing but the bulrush yonder."

Then they talked of Hiawatha's mother.

And Hiawatha cried out, "O Mudjekeewis! It was you who killed her!" The old man nodded silently, sadly.

Then Hiawatha sprang up. With his magic mittens he smashed a boulder apart and hurled the rocks at Mudjekeewis.

But the West Wind, breathing strongly, blew the rocks back at Hiawatha.

An eagle flapped his wings above them, screaming.

Now Mudjekeewis seized a giant bulrush. He battled Hiawatha with it, but the brave young Indian only laughed at him.

They fought there till the earth shook beneath their feet and the mountains thundered to the noise of battle.

At last Hiawatha drove his father to the gateway of the Sunset, to earth's farthest edge.

Then Mudjekeewis called, "Stop, my son, my Hiawatha! It's impossible to kill me, for I am immortal. I put you to this test to prove your courage. Go back now to your people! Clear their fishing grounds and rivers. Kill all the monsters and evil things, as I once killed the Great Bear."

Thus their battle ended, in the days long ago. But one can still see the giant bulrush growing by the ponds and rivers, and the black rocks lying in the valleys of the Rockies.

Then Hiawatha started homeward. His heart had cooled and his anger was forgotten. The land lay pleasant all about him.

Only once he paused, in the land of the Dacotahs, where the Falls of Minnehaha flashed and gleamed among the oak trees, laughed and leaped into the water. Here he stopped to buy some heads for his arrows. For here lived an old Arrow-maker skilled in making arrow-heads of great sharpness and smoothness. And the Arrow-maker's lovely daughter lived with him. Her laughter was as musical as the waterfall from which her father had named

her: Minnehaha, Laughing Water.

Was it really to buy arrow-heads that Hiawatha stopped in the land of the Dacotahs? Perhaps it was to see the lovely Indian maiden. Who shall say what thoughts and dreams filled the young man's heart when he saw Minnehaha?

But to old Nokomis, when he reached home, he told only of his meeting with his father. Not a word about arrows. Not a word of Laughing Water.

HIAWATHA'S FASTING

NOW Hiawatha went alone to the forest to fast. He built himself a wigwam. For seven days and nights he did not eat. He prayed, asking the Indian God Manito to show him how to help his people.

The first day, when the deer ran from him, he thought: "If the deer become too few, the Indians will starve."

The next day, when he saw the wild berries and the grapes, he thought: "When winter comes, there will be no more."

The third day, as he watched the fish swim in the sunny lake, he thought: "A hot summer might dry up the lakes and kill the fish. What, then, would the red men eat?"

On the fourth day, as he lay watching the setting sun, there suddenly appeared before him a young man dressed in green and yellow garments. Plumes of green bent over his forehead, and his hair was soft and golden.

"I am Mondamin," the young man said. "The Great Manito has sent me to tell you he has heard your prayers. The red men shall have food. But it will take struggle and labor. Come, now, and wrestle with me."

Hiawatha was weak from fasting, but he obeyed. And as he wrestled, his strength returned. Then Mondamin vanished—as quickly as if he had sunk into the ground.

Next day, at sunset, Mondamin came again and wrestled with Hiawatha; and the day after, they wrestled even longer. When they stopped, Mondamin smiled. "Tomorrow, Hiawatha, you will win," he told him. "Then, as I lie like one dead, strip me of my clothes and bury me. Make the ground above me soft and light. Watch carefully over me and let no weeds grow on that place, till I awake and leap into the sunshine."

All this Hiawatha did. He covered Mondamin with soft earth, kept it free of weeds and drove away the crows.

At last a small green shoot began to come up from the ground. Then another, and another. And before the summer ended, there were many fields of these beautiful plants, all taller than a man. They had green leaves and yellow tassels that waved behind them in the wind.

"It is Mondamin!" Hiawatha told his people.

Then he called to old Nokomis
And Iagoo, the great boaster,
Showed them where the maize was growing,
Told them of his wondrous vision,
Of his wrestling and his triumph,
Of this new gift to the nations,
Which should be their food forever.

And when autumn had turned the leaves to yellow, and the soft and juicy kernels grew hard and yellow, Hiawatha gathered the ripened ears of corn. He stripped off the withered husks, as he had once stripped the wrestler, and gave a big feast in honor of Mondamin.

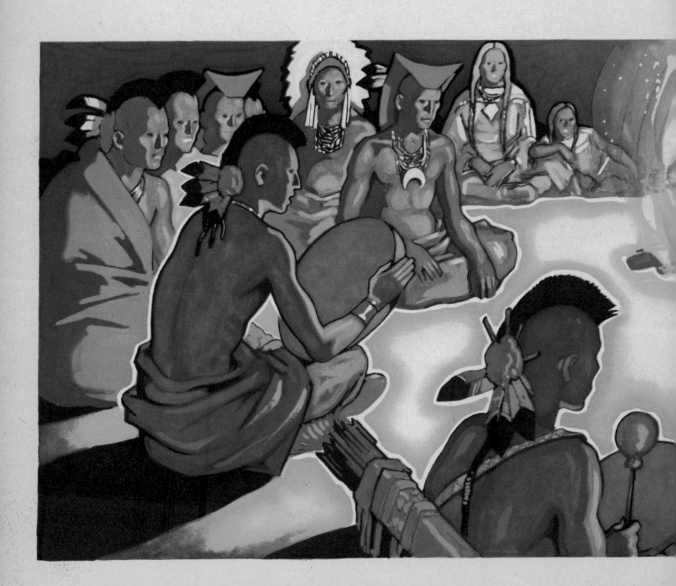

HIAWATHA'S SAILING

WHEN spring came Hiawatha planned to build a canoe. He went into the forest and as he walked he called to the trees.

"Give me of your bark, O Birch-Tree!
Of your yellow bark, O Birch-Tree!
Growing by the rushing river,
Tall and stately in the valley!
I a light canoe will build me,
Build a swift Cheemaun for sailing.
Lay aside your cloak, O Birch-Tree!
Lay aside your white-skin wrapper,
For the Summer-time is coming,
And the sun is warm in heaven,
And you need no white-skin wrapper!"

And the tree with all its branches
Rustled in the breeze of morning,
Saying with a sigh of patience,
"Take my cloak, O Hiawatha!"

So Hiawatha stripped a great piece of bark from the Birch-Tree. Then he went to another tree.

"Give me of your boughs, O Cedar!
Of your strong and pliant branches,
My canoe to make more steady,
Make more strong and firm beneath me!"

With the boughs from the cedar he made the framework of his canoe. The Larch-Tree gave him its tough roots to bind his canoe together. Again he asked:

"Give me of your balm, O Fir-Tree!
Of your balsam and your resin,
So to close the seams together
That the water may not enter
That the river may not wet me!"

Thus he built his birch canoe. To decorate it, the Hedgehog gave him all his quills. These Hiawatha stained red and blue and yellow with the juice of roots and berries, and strung them like a necklace around the canoe. Two stars decked its prow.

> Paddles none had Hiawatha,
> Paddles none he had or needed
> For his thoughts as paddles served him,
> And his wishes served to guide him;
> Swift or slow at will he glided,
> Veered to right or left at pleasure.

HIAWATHA'S FISHING

WITH a fishing-line made of the twisted bark of cedar, Hiawatha set forth to catch the giant sturgeon Nahma, King of Fishes. Alone he sat at the stern of his canoe. At the bow sat the squirrel, Adjidaumo.

As the canoe glided on the clear waters, Hiawatha saw Nahma lying on the white sands of the river bottom.

> "Take my bait," cried Hiawatha,
> Down into the depths beneath him,
> "Take my bait, O Sturgeon, Nahma!
> Come up from below the water,
> Let us see which is the stronger!"

But Nahma would not stir. Instead, he told the pike, "Take the bait of the rude fellow, break the line of Hiawatha!"

In his fingers Hiawatha felt the line jerk and tighten. As he drew it in, it tugged so that the birch canoe stood endwise, with the squirrel, Adjidaumo, perching and frisking on top.

When Hiawatha saw the pike rise upward, he was full of
scorn. He shouted through the water, "You are not the fish I
wanted!"

Then Nahma told the sun-fish, "Take the bait of this great

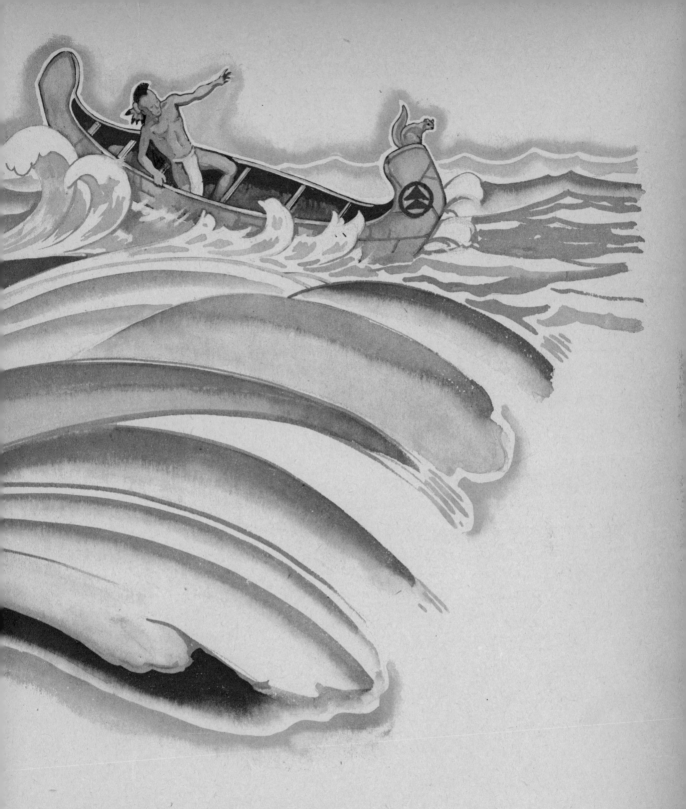

boaster, break the line of Hiawatha!"

The sun-fish made a whirlpool in the water, whirled the birch canoe in circles. But Hiawatha shouted, "You are not the fish I wanted!"

Now the giant sturgeon, very angry, darted upward. He leaped into the sunshine, opened his great jaws, and swallowed the canoe with Hiawatha in it.

Down, down inside the sturgeon plunged Hiawatha. There, in utter darkness, he groped about till he felt a great heart beating. Striking it again and again with his fist, he killed the mighty

King of Fishes. Then he dragged his canoe to a safe place deep inside the giant fish, while the squirrel, Adjidaumo, still frisking and chattering gaily, toiled and tugged with him. Hiawatha was grateful for his help, and said:

"O my little friend, the squirrel,
Bravely have you toiled to help me:
Take the thanks of Hiawatha,
And the name which now he gives you;
For hereafter and forever
Boys shall call you Adjidaumo,
Tail-in-air the boys shall call you!"

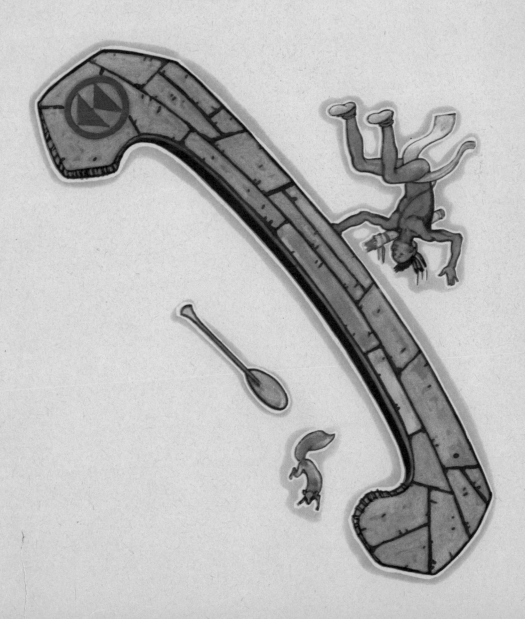

Now the sea-gulls came. And Hiawatha called to them to tear open the dead fish and set him free. "It's our brother, Hiawatha," they called to one another. Then with their sharp claws and beaks they tore apart the ribs of the giant fish and Hiawatha came safely out of his dark prison.

He called to old Nokomis, "I have killed the King of Fishes. I have killed the giant sturgeon, Nahma. Let the gulls feast upon him. Then do you strip the oily flesh from Nahma, and make oil for winter."

HIAWATHA AND THE PEARL-FEATHER

ONE day, as she stood on the shores of Gitche Gumee, Nokomis pointed westward with her finger and said to Hiawatha:

"Yonder lives the great Pearl-Feather, the Magician. Yonder, guarded by the black swamp water.

"He it was who killed my father. He sends fever from the marshes. He sends death among us.

"Take your bow, O Hiawatha. Take your arrows, take your war-club. The oil of Nahma smeared upon your birch canoe will make it slide through the black swamp water.

"Kill this cruel Magician, and save our people!"

Straightaway Hiawatha launched his birch canoe for sailing. "Onward, my canoe! he shouted, patting its sides with his palms.

All that night he sailed the black swamp water. The bullfrogs watched with yellow eyes. Mosquitoes sang their war-song.

As the sun rose on the water, the canoe leaped across the water lilies, through the tangled rushes, and landed Hiawatha on the beach beyond them. There stood the shining wigwam of the Magician.

Then Hiawatha shot a swift arrow at the wigwam, and shouted a challenge: "Come forth from your lodge, Pearl-Feather!"

"Well I know you, Hiawatha!" the Magician answered, in a voice of thunder. He stood there, dark and terrible in a magic shirt of wampum. "Hurry home, coward—before I kill you!"

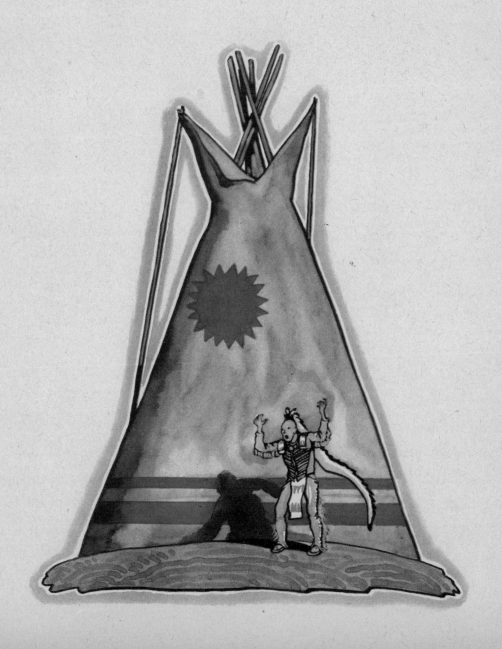

But Hiawatha answered, "Words are not as sharp as arrows." All that summer's day they fought. But Hiawatha's arrows could not pierce the magic shirt of wampum.

His war-club broken, Hiawatha paused at sunset beneath a pine tree. He was wounded and tired. What, now, could he do?

Suddenly, from a bough above him, Mama, the woodpecker, spoke softly. "Aim your arrows at the tuft of hair upon his head."

The Magician, stooping, raised a heavy stone to throw it.

Swiftly Hiawatha sent an arrow straight to the crown of the Magician's head. He shot another arrow, then his last. All his arrows pierced the spot where the bird had told him to aim.

And the great Magician lay lifeless at Hiawatha's feet, his magic broken.

In gratitude to the woodpecker, Hiawatha stained with blood the tuft of feathers on the bird's crown. That is why to this day the woodpecker wears a tuft of crimson feathers.

Then Hiawatha filled his canoe with riches from the Magician's wigwam—furs of beaver, sable and ermine, wampum belts and pouches, quivers filled with silver-headed arrows.

Homeward then he sailed. As his canoe landed on the shores of Gitche Gumee, there stood Nokomis and the others of his tribe waiting for him. They welcomed him with songs and dances, made a joyous feast, and shouted, "Honor be to Hiawatha!"

And Hiawatha divided with his people the riches he had brought from the wigwam of Pearl-Feather, the Magician.

HIAWATHA'S BRIDE

HIAWATHA dreamed still of Minnehaha, the lovely Laughing Water, daughter of the Arrow-maker in the land of the Dacotahs.

Nokomis tried to change his thoughts. "No matter how beautiful, she is a stranger," she warned. "Far better marry a maiden of your own tribe."

But Hiawatha answered, "Dear old Nokomis, our maidens are lovely, but my heart longs for Minnehaha."

"Hiawatha," Nokomis warned again, "she is a Dacotah, and the Dacotahs are very fierce. There is often war between them and our tribe."

"All the more reason for my marrying Laughing Water," Hiawatha told her. "That the two tribes shall be friends again, and all thought of war forgotten forever."

So he departed. With the moccasins of magic, he ran through the forest lightly as a breeze is blown. On he ran until he heard the cheerful voice of the Falls of Minnehaha where the Arrow-

maker lived.

Then he killed a deer, a gift for Laughing Water, and swung it across his shoulder.

The old Arrow-maker was sitting in the doorway of his wigwam. Laughing Water sat beside him. With her hands she braided mats of grass. But her thoughts were of the handsome hunter she had seen one day.

> She had heard her father praise him,
> Praise his courage and his wisdom.
> Would he come again for arrows
> To the Falls of Minnehaha?

For a while her hands lay idle as she dreamed of Hiawatha. Suddenly he stood before them.
"Welcome, Hiawatha!" said the Arrow-maker.

Hiawatha laid the deer at the feet of Laughing Water. The maiden looked up at him and said gently, "You are welcome, Hiawatha."

Then they went into the wigwam. Laughing Water brought food, and water from the brooklet. She listened while the guest was speaking, listened while her father answered

Hiawatha told of old Nokomis, who had nursed him in his childhood. He told of his good friends. He told of happiness and plenty in the land of the Ojibways that was his home. He spoke of the peace that now prevailed between the Dacotahs and the Ojibways.

Finally he came to his errand:

"That this peace may last forever
And our hands be clasped more closely
And our hearts be more united
Give me as my wife this maiden
Minnehaha, Laughing Water!"

The Arrow-maker looked proudly at Hiawatha, and fondly at his daughter. Then he smoked awhile in silence.

At last he said, "Let your heart speak, Minnehaha!"

Then lovely Laughing Water went to Hiawatha and sat down beside him. Shyly she answered, "I will marry Hiawatha—I will follow you, my husband."

Hand in hand, they left the wigwam. Hand in hand, they walked together through the forest. Hiawatha carried Minnehaha across the rushing streams in their pathway. In his strong arms, she seemed lighter than a willow leaf.

The sun shone, and the birds sang sweetly. The rabbits hopped

down the path before them.

At night, Hiawatha made a bough bed for Minnehaha. And the squirrel, Adjidaumo, kept watch over her while she slept.

Thus it was they journeyed homeward. Thus it was that Hiawatha brought his bride to the lodge of old Nokomis.

HIAWATHA'S WEDDING FEAST

OLD NOKOMIS prepared a sumptuous wedding feast. And the guests came in all their richest raiment.

They had fish and deer meat, and cakes of yellow corn. They had wild honey, berries, and sugar made of maple sap. The men smoked willow bark in their red-stone pipes.

Then Nokomis asked the Storm-Fool to dance for them. He wore leggings trimmed with beads. He had braided his long hair with sweet grass. And he danced till the leaves whirled with him.

The sweetest of the Ojibway musicians sang his love songs. And the beavers left their lodges that they might listen.

Happy days followed. Hiawatha found a way to put down his thoughts in picture writing. And Minnehaha blessed the corn.

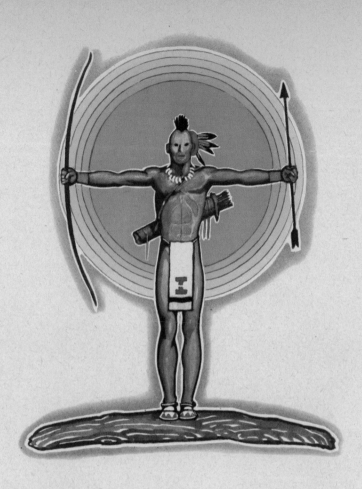

THE COMING OF THE WHITE MAN

ONE day Iagoo, the boaster, returned from a journey, saying:
"I have seen a body of water bigger than the Big-Sea-Water.
And a great canoe with wings that flew."

The red men laughed at him. All except Hiawatha.

"It is true," he told his people. "For I have seen it in a dream.
I have seen the great canoe of the white-faced people. I saw too,
in that dream, the coming to this land of many people from other,
crowded nations. All the land was full of people, restless, strug-
gling, toiling, striving, speaking many different languages, yet feel-
ing as one in their love for this country.

Let us welcome, then, the strangers,
Hail them as our friends and brothers,
And the heart's right hand of friendship
Give them when they come to see us.
Gitche Manito, the Mighty,
Said this to me in my vision.

"But in this dream I saw, too, a darker, drearier vision. I saw our nation scattered, all forgetting my counsels, weakened by warring with each other. I saw the remnants of our people being swept westward like the withered leaves of Autumn!"

Hiawatha bade his people listen to the message of hope the white men would bring to these shores.

Then, one day, Hiawatha told his people that he must go on a long journey and that it would be many years before he returned to them. Standing on the shore, he waved his hand in farewell. Then he shoved his birch-canoe out onto the clear water.

And the evening sun descending
Set the clouds on fire with redness,
Burned the broad sky, like a prairie,
Left upon the level water
One long track and trail of splendor,
Down whose stream, as down a river,
Westward, westward Hiawatha
Sailed into the fiery sunset,
Sailed into the purple vapors,
Sailed into the dusk of evening.

The Story of
HIAWATHA